Let's Break the Record

HarperCollinsChildren'sBooks

First published in India in 2022 by **HarperCollins Children's Books**
An imprint of HarperCollins *Publishers*
Building No 10, Tower A, 4th Floor,
DLF Cyber City, Phase II, Gurugram 122002
www.harpercollins.co.in

2 4 6 8 10 9 7 5 3 1

P-ISBN: 9789356293762
E-ISBN: 9789356293779

Typeset in CookieRunOTF 14 pt/24 by **Shamika Chaves**

Printed and bound by Nutech Print Services – India

HarperCollinsIn

Ricky

MUHAHAHA! You may know Pang as
the group leader, but the true leader
is me! You'll understand if you stick
around! HAHAHA!

Oliver

What great weather we have today.
On a day like this, I just want to sit by the lake,
eat cookies, and listen to some music.
So... Please don't take my cookies!

Shasha

I can make anything I put
my mind to! So tell me
what you need.
But don't go asking for
too much, okay?

PANG

I like anything fun! Join me
if you are feeling down.
PANG! A game of cricket
will help you feel better!

Cash

Let's go play right now!!
It'll be fun! Quickly!
Cash has lots of great ideas!

While playing cricket
with his friends,
Cash caught a ball
that was high up in the air.
"Yahoo! I set a new record!"
Cash shouted.

"A new record?"

Pang asked.

Cash showed his

record-keeping notebook

to his friends.

The notebook had
pictures of all
the records Cash had set.
**"If you guys set
a new record, I'll write
it in my notebook
as well!"** said Cash.

"Then let's spend today setting new records!" said Shasha.

Ricky, Shasha, Pang,
and Oliver were standing
in a line with a bat in their hand.
"Ready! Set! Go!" Cash shouted.
He was the referee.

The first activity was bouncing a cricket ball.
Pang set the record for bouncing the ball the longest.

Pang, Ricky, and Oliver tried
their best, but it wasn't easy.

The second activity was long jump.
Ricky was very good, but Shasha was even better.

Shasha easily took the record
for the longest jump.

The third activity was reading.
Ricky was confident that
he was the fastest reader.

Oliver was not very confident,
but he tried his best.
In the end, Ricky set the record
for reading the fastest.

The next activity was shouting
the longest without taking a breath.
Oliver was sure he could set the new record,
but the record went to Ricky.

Ricky cheated by poking Oliver in the side.
Oliver was not happy with Ricky.

Soon Ricky realized what he had done was wrong.
Ricky visited Oliver to apologize for cheating,
but Oliver was very upset.

Ricky tried his best to make
Oliver feel better, but it did not work.

Oliver was alone in the woods
when Ricky sneakily followed him there.

Ricky saw Oliver throw an apple
far into the sky and had a brilliant idea.
Oliver was a brilliant bowler.

Ricky called his friends over for
one last record-setting activity.
The activity was throwing a ball to pop balloons.

Ricky knew Oliver was going to win this record.

In the end,
Oliver was finally able to
set a new record thanks to Ricky.

Ricky set a new record as well.
A record for taking the longest time
to make a friend feel better.

The **Cricket Pang** series is a set of picture books with charming stories based on lovable animal characters. The overall theme of the books is cricket, which besides being a very popular sport for children, also lends a unique flavour to this series. Children will love the main character, Pang, and his bunch of friends. Each book highlights important values through engaging stories and endearing characters. With their simple vocabulary and sentence structure, these books are perfect for early readers.

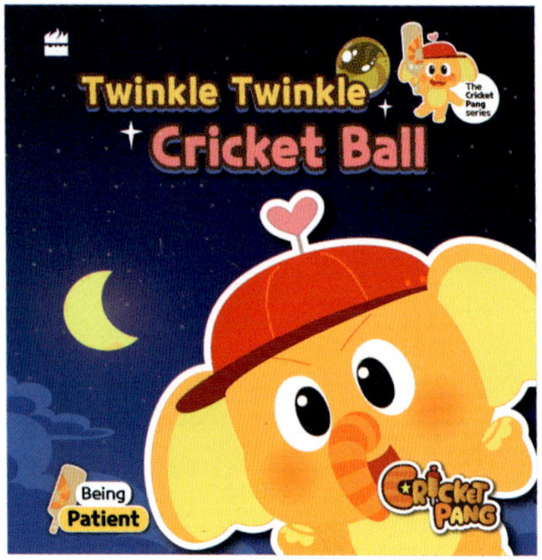

Being patient!

Being fun!

Being kind!

Being smart!

Follow our **YouTube Channel [CricketPang TV]** for more Cricket Pang content.
(QR code on the back cover)